An Angel Came

BEVERLY PIGUE

Trilogy Christian Publishers
A Wholly Owned Subsidary of Trinity Broadcasting Network
2442 Michelle Drive
Tustin, CA 92780

For information, address Trilogy Christian Publishing
Rights Department, 2442 Michelle Drive, Tustin, Ca 92780.
Trilogy Christian Publishing/ TBN and colophon are trademarks of Trinity Broadcasting Network.

For information about special discounts for bulk purchases, please contact Trilogy Christian Publishing.

Manufactured in the United States of America

10 9 8 7 6 5 4 3 2 1

Library of Congress Cataloging-in-Publication Data is available.

ISBN 978-1-64773-112-0 (Print Book)
ISBN 978-1-64773-113-7 (ebook)

DEDICATION

This book is dedicated to all those who would listen and hear the quiet whispers of the Holy Spirit. May His guidance ease your path and His words heal your heart as you walk through life. For those that have yet to walk with our Lord, perhaps this will open your eyes to the love that is yours through Him.

Just as I have been with Moses, I will be with you; I will not fail you or forsake you. Joshua 1:5

PREFACE

This book is a collection of the quiet whispers of the Holy Spirit giving me words until I took the time to write them down. I did not set out to create these stories, but merely heard them, and I will take credit for that; though, I wish to make it clear that, of myself, I could not possibly have invented them. I thank those around me, my family and friends, that encouraged me to take a step out of the box and share words that were clearly not mine, but of our Lord—words meant to help and to heal, words meant to ease and to console.

CONTENTS

JAY AND THE EARTH SUIT

Jay was a big boy
Nearly 5 years old
His family thought him smart
Or so he was told

But he didn't understand
About death and such
His family was sad
They didn't offer him much

He wanted to ask them
But prayed instead
For someone to help him
This is what he said

"Please, Father God, explain to me
So I might know just what they mean
Aunt Freida died, she's gone away
But what does that mean,
what does that say?"

And so that night
An angel came
She said to Jay
"Let's play a game

See in the mirror
The sight you see
It's not really who
You are to me

So look real deep
Into the eyes
Then you'll see
A big surprise"

Jay looked real hard
But didn't see
He told the angel
"That's just me"

She smiled and said
"Now look once more"
Jay looked back
And his eyes explored

Then he saw
The image changed
A shimmering light
Seemed to arrange

It blurred and shined
So very bright
It blocked all out
This amazing light

"See," said the angel
"This is thee
The truth of who
You really be

This light eternal
Is your spirit, your true
It rests within
What you think is you

5

But really just a body
To wear and to play
While you're on Earth
A visit, a stay"

As Jay saw the vision
The light so bright
He remembered it all
His truth, his right

And he knew death
Was a time to be glad
A celebration of love
And happiness not sad

"Now look to the eyes,"
Said the angel, "and see
The truth of all people
And the light they be"

Jay sat quietly
And looked all around
My family is sad
He thought with a frown

But he couldn't be sad
He just didn't see
The sadness they felt
So he tried to be

9

But it just didn't work
Cause inside he knew
Aunt Freida had died
Her task on Earth through

A celebration he thought
A party for she
Who still lives on
In the light she be

Each day after that
Jay looked to the eyes
He saw the truth
And light, no lies

He thought of Aunt Freida
And what it did mean
The fact that she died
Or so it did seem

But he thought with a smile
I will see her again
When my life here is done
And I'm light once again.

SALLY AND HER FEELINGS

Sally was sad
And alone and afraid
Her sweet doggy Pumkin
Had died that day

Though sad was she
No one seemed to hear
The feelings she felt
For her doggy dear

They acted as if
Nothing happened that day
Seemed no one cared
At least she saw it that way

Then mad was she
At Pumkin, at the world
So many feelings she had
Her emotions swirled

She held them all in
Held them tight, did not cry
But each day that passed
A piece of her died

She changed from happy
To angry and mean
She acted all out
In tantrums, she screamed

Then an angel appeared
At night while she slept
She touched Sally's cheek
To tears where she wept

"Sally," she said,
"Can I share with you
A tool I know
To be part of your true?

You must feel what you feel
Don't hide it inside
Be angry, be sad
If you need to cry

Don't hide it away
For it only comes back
In anger and hurt
And a need to attack

These feelings you feel
Will lessen each day
If only you feel them
Then they'll be cleansed away

You'll feel better inside
Then outside too
In no time at all
Perhaps a smile for you"

Sally said, "Okay
I will give it a try"
Then she cried some tears
And gave a big sigh

19

She noticed her heart
Was lighter each day
Though she still missed Pumkin
Her sadness didn't stay

And remembered did she
All the love that they shared
All the good times and fun
And an angel who cared.

AMY'S GRANDMA

Amy had a grandma
Her smile so very sweet
With fluffy white hair
She kept it very neat

But she didn't remember
Many times she was confused
Her mind seemed to wander
Her memory she did lose

"I don't understand!"
Amy yelled out to the sky
"Does she even know I love her?
Can someone tell me why?"

And then an angel came
While sleeping in the night
She had a loving glow
That Amy thought so bright

"Amy," she did say
"Perhaps what we could see
When looking at your grandma
Is the truth of who she be

The whole of all her true
Not just the suit we see
When looking with our eyes
There's so much more she be

Your grandma, like all man
Was born through love from He
Our Father in the heavens
His love is all we be

And though her body suit
Seems damaged, it's okay
Her spirit is eternal
In love embraced each day"

Amy sat so quiet
Her grandma by her side
She thought about the lesson
Though still it made her cry

Quite suddenly an image
It flashed into her mind
Of Grandma light surrounding
And smiling oh so kind

"Amy," she did hear
"I'm safe and unafraid
Embraced in all God's glory
And the loving He has made"

And though her eyes did cry
Amy's smile began that day
She knew her Grandma's spirit
Was safe and on her way

And the earth suit left behind
Was not all there was to see
For now she looked beyond
To God's truth of eternity.